LARA KIOSSES

**Self-taught photographer
Lara Kiosses was born in Paris and
raised in Africa. Curious about
different worlds and fascinated by
people and their histories, she aims
to immortalise these in a nearly
obsessive way.**

It starts with a man, of course.

Some then imagine a saccharine romance, one sweet kiss, full of promises.

At first, skin purrs, of course. No flaws anymore, only the memory of his lips.

But little by little, you start asking yourself... Was I a crush? Was it fate or just a fling?

The very same kiss ends up stealing your sleep and you spend your nights shaking like a barfly.

Is he with her?

Then the silences come and those mornings spent as strangers again...
As if something had changed...
her perfume floating in the air.

The first French-kiss is now only a distant memory, a story of neurobiology, from which love is excluded forever more.

Paris 7 am
This city soon
will become
the memory
of a love story.

I imagine him with another woman.

Suddenly everything is amplified: anger and jealousy.

I would like to know everything about it;

sometimes then I think about it too much and my body reacts, refuses.

Did he like kissing them; did it matter to him?

In which ways did his hands caress all those bodies that were not mine?

Oh how we loved each other so... Oh how I have hated him.

How many smiles and promises...

Love is adrift, feelings illusory

COLOPHON

Photography and text by **Lara Kiosses**
www.larakiosses.com

Published by **New Heroes & Pioneers**
Model inside pages is **Alexandra Langlais**
Model cover is **Garance Rochoux-Moreau**

Co-edited by **Emma Hansson**
and Francois Le Bled

Creative Direction by **Jens Lennartsson**
Book design by **Lara Caputo**

Printed by ThePrintlink (Denmark)

Legal deposit January 2015

ISBN 978-91-878150-2-7

new Heroes & Pioneers.